# Me and My Cousin

Written by Amanda Rainger
Illustrated by Simone Abel

WAYLAND

My cousin Jamila
is my best friend.

She lives on our street,
in the house at the end.

I meet up with Jamila
at school every day.

We like it the best,
when we go out to play.

When we play chase,
we run and we shout.

Jamila catches me,
and then I am out!

We jump on the numbers,
and count up to ten.

"One... two... three..."
Then we do it again.

Look in the playground,
and you will see...

all of my friends,
and Jamila and me.

We go to the park,
and we play on the swings.

We fly up and down,
and pretend we have wings.

We spin round and round.
We go ever so fast.

But Jamila stays on,
so that she is the last.

1

When we get off,
we always fall down.

We climb up and up,
and look over the wall.

We see people shopping.
The cars look so small.

Look in the park,
and you will see...

all of my friends,
and Jamila and me.

**START READING** is a series of highly enjoyable books for beginner readers. **The books have been carefully graded to match the Book Bands widely used in schools.** This enables readers to be sure they choose books that match their own reading ability.

### Look out for the Band colour on the book in our Start Reading logo.

The Bands are:

Pink Band 1A & 1B

Red Band 2

Yellow Band 3

Blue Band 4

Green Band 5

Orange Band 6

Turquoise Band 7

Purple Band 8

Gold Band 9

**START READING** books can be read independently or shared with an adult. They promote the enjoyment of reading through satisfying stories supported by fun illustrations.

**Amanda Rainger** writes books and TV programmes for children learning French and Spanish. Best of all, she likes making up songs and stories – especially in rhyme! She works in a shed in the garden, with a tortoise, a fox and a chaffinch for company.

**Simone Abel** has illustrated over 200 books for children and has even won some awards. Best of all, she likes drawing people and animals, although she has just finished illustrating a book about cakes, which was great fun! She lives in Yorkshire, with her husband who is a painter, and their two daughters.